This book belongs to:

Name _____

Age _____

My favourite Disney character is:

_____

Editor: Anne Ewart   Designer: Martin Shubrook

£5.99
UK only

C000156247

Disney and Me Annual 2001

Contents

The elephant's hair

Tarzan's best friend, Terk, was going exploring in the jungle with two of her gorilla playmates, Flynt and Mungo. Tarzan wanted to go with them and join in their adventure but

Mungo and Flynt didn't want Tarzan tagging along behind. "He's too small to be any fun. We'll have to keep stopping to let him catch up with us," they said.

Terk knew how to get rid of Tarzan. "If you want to join in with us, you have to bring back an elephant's hair from the lagoon at the bottom of the waterfall!" she said.

Terk and her friends thought that Tarzan would give up and go home, but they were wrong. Tarzan let out a big yell as he rushed past them and leaped into the lagoon.

Tarzan began swimming towards the herd of elephants. "Piranhas! Everybody run!" yelled Tantor, a nervous, young elephant, when he saw Tarzan under the water.

Suddenly, Tarzan jumped up and grabbed one of the elephants' tails. The whole herd trumpeted in panic and began to splash about and stampede out of the lagoon.

Up on the cliff, Terk, Flynt and Mungo watched, as the herd of elephants charged right through the area where the other gorillas were feeding. "Oh, no, look at the trouble we've caused! We shouldn't have set Tarzan such an impossible task!" groaned Terk. They rushed down to the lagoon to make sure that Tarzan was all right.

When they reached him, Tarzan held out his hand. "I did it! I got the elephant's hair. Can I join in with you now?" he spluttered. The three gorillas gasped in amazement.

"Be careful, that piranha will bite you!" cried Tantor, still thinking that Tarzan was dangerous. "Tarzan's not a piranha. He's an ape, just like us," replied Terk, smiling.

About the story

1. What are Terk's friends' names?
2. Why did Terk ask Tarzan to fetch an elephant's hair?
3. How did Tarzan get into the lagoon?
4. Who thought Tarzan was a piranha?
5. Where did the elephant herd charge through?

Answers:
1) Flynt and Mungo. 2) She thought that Tarzan would give up and go home. 3) Tarzan leaped off the cliff. 4) Tantor. 5) The gorillas' feeding area.

Jungle search

Tarzan and his friends have gone exploring in the jungle. Can you count how many butterflies and bananas they saw on their travels?

Answer: Five butterflies and eight bananas.

A splashing time

Tarzan has completed the tough challenge set by Terk and her friends. Now it's your turn to complete these tricky teasers.

1 Which gorilla is holding up three fingers?

2 Which two flowers add up to the same amount?

3 What type of creature is swimming under the water?

4 How many elephants can you count?

5 Is Tarzan holding the hair in his left or right hand?

6 Can you spot five differences in Tantor's reflection?

Answers:
1) a. 2) b and c. 3) A turtle. 4) 8. 5) Right. 6) His trunk is curled more, he's looking in a different direction, he's eating leaves, he has a flower on his tail, one of his hairs is missing.

11

Aping around

Jane loves playing with the baby gorillas. Join in with their fun by finding the answers to these three puzzles.

1 Which of these close-ups doesn't appear in the picture?

a

b

c

d

2 Starting with **JANE**, put these words in order so that only one letter changes each time.

**JANE CANS CANE
PINS PANS**

3 Can you think of three names beginning with **J** to call the baby gorillas?

Answers: 1) c. 2) JANE, CANE, CANS, PANS, PINS.

12

A jungle journal

Jane likes to write about her jungle adventures in her journal. Help her finish writing about her day by using the spare words on the page to fill in the blank spaces.

baboons

fruit

pencils

I was looking at some beautiful

when I spotted a

eating some

 .

I drew a picture of it in my

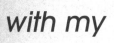

with my

 .

Suddenly, lots of other

appeared. My, what a sight!

butterflies

book

baby baboon

Picture

THE STORY

1) The toys watched through the binoculars as Woody was stolen by a greedy toy collector.

2) By decoding some letters from the toy collector's car, Buzz found out that Woody had been taken to Al's Toy Barn.

3) The toys had great fun driving around Al's Toy Barn, looking for Woody. But they couldn't find him!

4) The toys went to look for Woody in the toy collector's apartment, high up in a block of flats.

5) Eventually, the toys found Woody and some new friends, too - Bullseye the horse and Jessie the cowgirl.

6) The toys made it back to Andy's room... just in time to welcome Andy back from Cowboy Camp!

a

c

e

Answers:
1) a. 2) e. 3) f. 4) b. 5) c. 6) d.

perfect

b

d

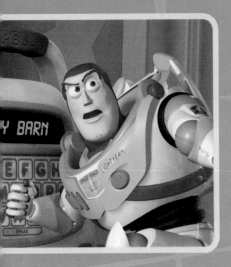

f

Ready, set, go!

Buzz and his friends are on an exciting adventure to rescue Woody. Play this game with your friends to see who will be the champion cone carrier.

START 1 2 3 4

drop

11 10 go 8 7 6

12

13 14 drop

16

go

18 19 20 21

You will need: a dice and a counter for each player.

How to play

Place all the counters at the start, next to Buzz. Take turns to roll the dice and move your counter along the numbered spaces. If you land on a **drop** space you must miss a turn. If you land on a **go** space you must move forward one space. The first person to reach Woody is the winner, but watch out for the chewing gum!

29 30 31 drop

SPLAT!
Go back
to START.

27   33

            34

go   go

25   36

                FINISH

24   37   41

p 23   38 drop 40

Toy teasers

There's always something going on when the toys are in town. Can you answer each of these tricky toy teasers?

1 Which shadow matches Jessie exactly?

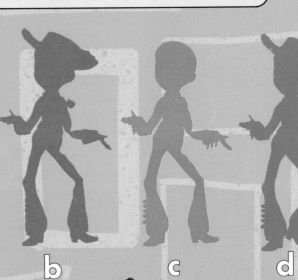

a   b   c   d

2 Draw a line to match each of these words to what they are.

slurp   •   • a gooey ooze

slug   •   • how a snake moves

slime   •   • a slimy creature

slither   •   • a drinking noise

3 Can you help Slinky think of four more words that begin with "**sl**"?

Answers: 1) a. 2) slurp - a drinking noise, slug - a slimy creature, slime - a gooey ooze, slither - how a snake moves.

18

The one and only

Buzz Lightyear has been surrounded by impostors! Can you spot the real Buzz Lightyear? He is the only one that matches his picture exactly.

(a)

(b)

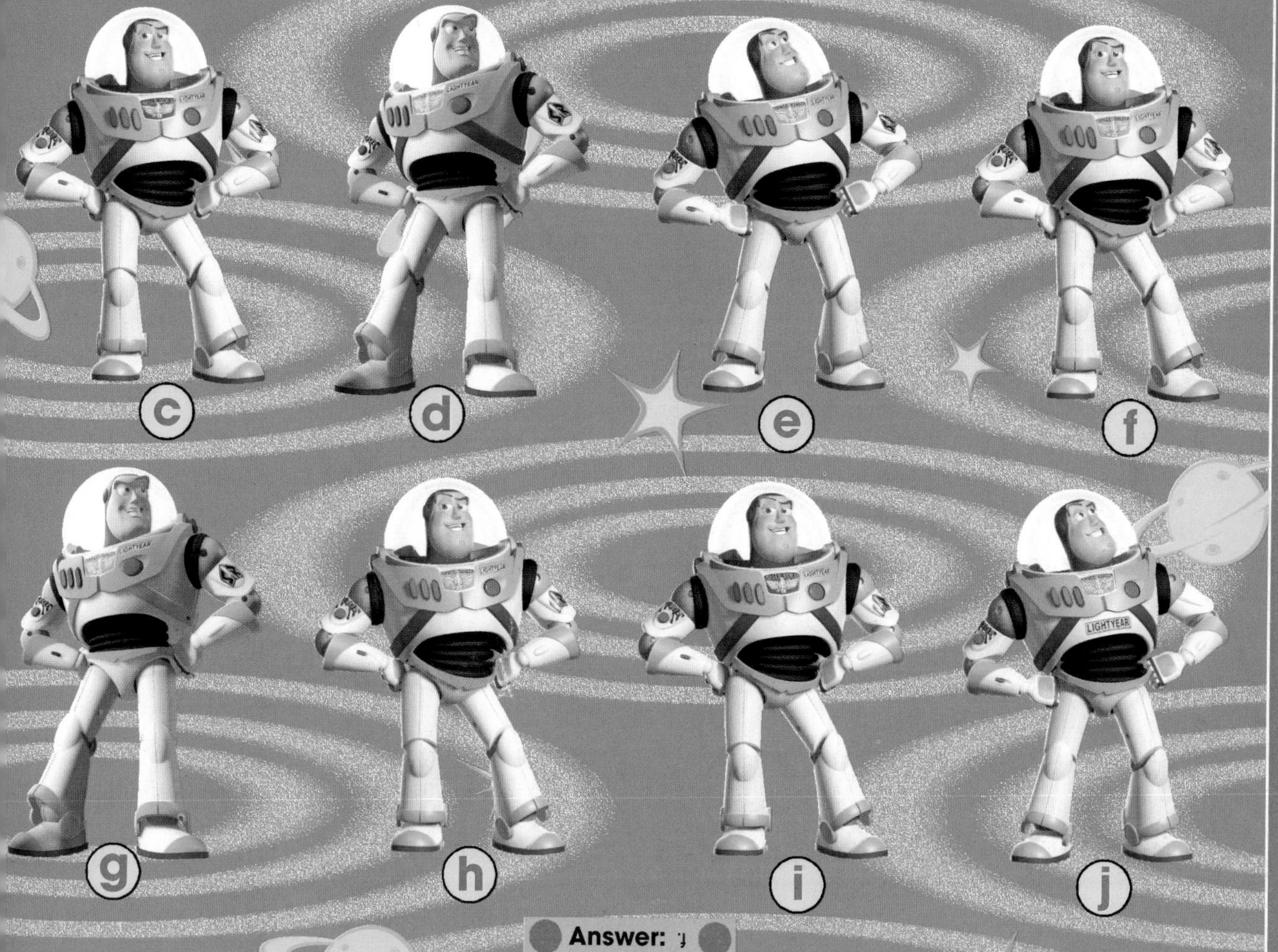

(c)

(d)

(e)

(f)

(g)

(h)

(i)

(j)

Answer: j

The Baduns had captured the puppies in Hell Hall, and had spent all afternoon teasing them. "We might as well have a bit of a snooze before Cruella arrives," said Jasper. Horace and Jasper slumped into big armchairs and fell asleep. "Let's teach those two big bullies a lesson," said Patch, as he explored the room.

Patch had a look in one of the drawers. He wagged his tail and whispered, "Hey, come and see what I've found." The puppies all rushed over to have a look.

When Jasper woke up, he felt a bit hungry. He reached over for his sandwich and took a bite. "Yuk!" he shouted. "This sandwich is covered with spots!"

"Blugh! My sandwiches must have gone off," said Jasper. "I need to have a drink." He went to take a drink, but the bottle was spotty as well! Jasper quickly went over to Horace. "I think we've been around these horrible puppies too long," he said. "Their spots are catching!" The puppies giggled.

"Don't be daft," laughed Horace. "You can't catch Dalmatian spots." "Then why do you have them on your face?" asked Jasper sarcastically.

"You do, too," snapped Horace. "We've got Dalmatian-itis!" shrieked Jasper. "Cruella will make coats out of us if she sees these spots!" cried Horace.

The puppies crowded around Jasper and Horace. "Keep away from us!" they shouted as they unlocked the door and ran out. The puppies rolled about laughing. "Jasper and Horace will kick themselves when they realise that their Dalmatian-itis is only ink that we flicked on them with our tails!"

About the story

1. Where were the Baduns keeping the puppies?
2. What was wrong with Jasper's sandwich?
3. Where were Horace's spots?
4. What did the Baduns think they had caught?
5. What really made the spots?

Answers:
1) Hell Hall. 2) It was covered in spots. 3) On his face. 4) Dalmatian-itis. 5) Ink.

Spots and dots

**The Dalmatian puppies find spots and dots wherever they go!
Here are some dotty puzzles for you to discover.**

1. Look at the white squares on the left for ten seconds. Then look at the black squares on the right. Dark spots will magically appear where the white lines cross.

2. Is the square with the thick line on the side of the box, or on the bottom? If you stare at the spot, the box will keep changing every few seconds.

Cruella's visit

**Cruella wants to buy the puppies,
but Roger and Anita have told her that the puppies are not for sale!**

1 Which puppy is being held by Cruella?

a   b

a   b   c   d   e

2 Which of these objects is not in the scene?

3 What time is it?

4 How many flowers are there?

5 Which of these bags belongs to Cruella?

Answers:
1.b. 2.d 3.4:00. 4.15 5.d

25

Mulan's army

Mulan and three other soldiers had been sent across the mountains to collect supplies for the army camp. As they made their way back towards the camp with their full cart, they came to a narrow path. "Let's stop here and have something to eat," said Mulan. She cut up a loaf of bread and spread honey on the slices.

As they ate, Mulan heard something. "What's that noise?" she asked the other soldiers. Everyone stopped eating and listened. There was a faint rumbling sound which was becoming louder and louder. Soon the noise was louder than thunder and it was making the ground shake.

Mulan looked up and shouted, "Look out, everyone! It's an avalanche!" They all hid under the cart as huge boulders tumbled past them and disappeared down the side of the mountain. The very last boulder to fall crashed on to the road right in front of their cart. It completely blocked the path. "Oh no!" cried Ling. "How are we going to get the supplies back to the camp?"

Yao replied, "If we use our strength, we'll soon shift it." They all began to push as hard as they could. They groaned and grunted, but the boulder didn't even move an inch. Yao looked at Mulan and said, "If you weren't so skinny, we would be able to move it."

Ling shook his head and said, "It's not anyone's fault. We'd need a whole army to shift that lump." Chien-Po sighed and said, "And to make matters worse, my bread and honey has been covered in dirt!" Yao, Ling and Chien-Po tried to push the boulder again.

Mulan looked at the slices of bread on the ground. She was amazed when one of the tiny ants crawled under a slice of bread and lifted it up. Mulan suddenly knew exactly what to do to move the boulder. She rummaged in the back of the cart and found a large pot. Then she climbed on to the boulder and said, "Stand back, everyone!" Mulan tipped the pot, and a gallon of honey poured over the boulder.

The honey slowly dribbled down the sides of the boulder. "How is making it sticky going to make the boulder any easier to move?" asked Ling. Mulan smiled and said, "You said we'd need a whole army to move it, and you were right!"

As she spoke, the little ant reappeared. But this time it was followed by hundreds of other ants. They marched straight towards the honey-coated boulder and surrounded it. Within moments, the group of ants had lifted up the boulder and carried it away. Mulan and the others jumped into the cart and carried on towards the army camp. Yao nudged Mulan and grinned, "You may not have very strong muscles, but you have a very strong mind!"

the end

Rice riddles

Mulan is working hard, but she can still find time for some fun and games!

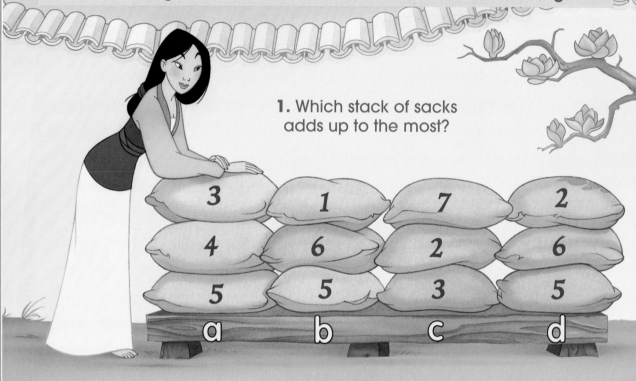

1. Which stack of sacks adds up to the most?

a	b	c	d
3	1	7	2
4	6	2	6
5	5	3	5

2. Little Brother weighs 6 kilograms. Which two sacks will balance the scale?

2kg
3kg
4kg
5kg

3. Is there an odd or even amount of rice grains?

Answers:
1. d. 2. 2 and 4kg. 3. Odd.

Mushu's mysteries

When he's not causing mischief, Mushu likes to solve perplexing puzzles.
See if you can help him find the answers to these three teasers.

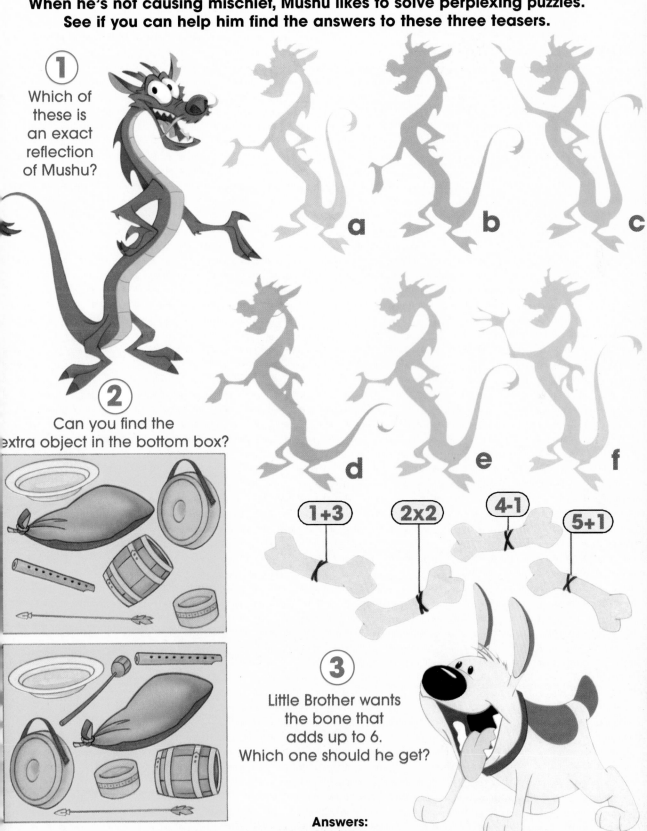

1 Which of these is an exact reflection of Mushu?

a   b   c

d   e   f

2 Can you find the extra object in the bottom box?

1+3   2x2   4-1   5+1

3 Little Brother wants the bone that adds up to 6. Which one should he get?

Answers:
1. e. 2. Gong stick. 3. 5+1

29

Spot the spy

Captain Shang has found out there is a Hun spy amongst his men, but he isn't sure which one it is. Can you help Shang find the spy by using the clues below?

The Hun spy is standing to the left of the soldier who is six places to the right of Mulan.

Mulan's map

Like all good soldiers, Mulan can read a map.
Why don't you try? If you were standing where the X is on the
map, which directions would the four views
at the bottom be - north, south, east or west?

Answers
1. South. 2. West. 3. North. 4. East.

31

Fight fair and square

It looks like Captain Hook has failed to outsmart Peter Pan yet again!
Are you smart enough to find the three pairs of identical squares?

Answer: 1a and 1g, 8a and 9c, 8b and 9g.

Hook can't lift a book

Peter Pan has challenged Captain Hook to pick up a book. Hook thought it would be easy, but it's much harder than it looks!

You will need two metres of strong string and a heavy book.

1. Tie the string around the book.

2. Ask each of your friends to stand up, one at a time, and hold one end of the string in each hand.

3. Now challenge them to pull the string out straight, while lifting the book at the same time.

4. No matter how hard they try, they will not be able to keep the string straight and lift the book.

Pirate's tre

When Captain Hook and his crew are
not chasing Peter Pan,
they are out hunting for treasure
to fill their pirate's chest.
Why not make your very own treasure
chest to store all your valuables?
Be sure to ask a grown-up to help you.

What you will need:
2 cardboard boxes
scissors
a pen or pencil
glue
masking tape
paints
string

1 Cut off one large flap,
and both small ones.

Cut open the second box, leaving the
bottom, and two short sides. Draw a half-
circle on each of the short sides.
Don't throw away the long side you have
cut off.

 Cut around the curves of the two half-
circles. Fold them back into an upright
position. Take one of the long sides you
cut away and tape it down the centre
for support.

asure chest

4 Cut a 24inch, or 60cm square of cardboard. Carefully bend it over the frame you have made. Glue the sides down and secure with masking tape.

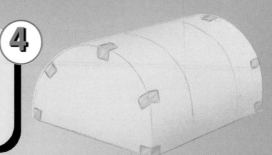

5 On the first box, cut a square away from the middle of the remaining flap, to make two hinges. Glue the lid on to the hinges and leave to dry.

6 Paint the outside of the chest with a keyhole and some pirate designs. Add different coloured sticky tape, to create a barrel effect.

7 Finally, line the chest with red cloth or shiny paper. Fix some string to each side of the lid. Now you are ready to fill your personal pirate treasure chest!

Rough and tumble

Peter Pan and The Lost Boys play all day long!
Join in with them as they find fun in the forest.

Cubby

Rabbit

1 Whose arrow will hit the bull's-eye?

3 Where is Peter's shadow?

How many arrows can you find?

4 Which sword is the longest?

OHOK

HOJN

ENTBILLREK

LICMAEH

YDNWE

5 Who is winning the tug of war?

6 Whose names are on the signpost?

b

37

The flying lion

Simba was out exploring one day, and as usual, Zazu was following him. "I'll be able to go wherever I want when I'm king," said Simba. "Not necessarily," boasted Zazu.

Zazu landed on a rock and added, "For instance, a lion can't fly to the top of a tree, like I can." Then he flew up to the highest branch in a nearby tree.

"I'll teach Zazu not to be such a show-off," Simba thought to himself. He began to walk away towards the watering hole to find one of his friends.

"I'm still watching you, Simba!" Zazu called down from the tree. "Well, I'm not going very far," said Simba. Zazu watched as Simba walked along the watering hole.

But the hot afternoon sun began to make Zazu feel very drowsy. "I'll just take a short nap," thought Zazu, as he snuggled in the leaves.

"Hello, Zazu!" said Simba. "I thought I'd fly up here and join you for a nap!" Zazu nearly fell out of the tree with shock. "I must be dreaming," he thought.

Zazu rubbed his eyes in disbelief, "A flying lion? The heat of the sun has played tricks with my mind." Zazu flew off in a fluster to look for some shade.

But Simba didn't really fly up to the top of the tree - a tall giraffe lifted Simba up! "That will keep Zazu from boasting that he's the only one who can fly," laughed Simba.

Jungle jigsaw

There's been a bit of a mix-up with these three Pride Land pictures.
Can you find where the nine jigsaw pieces belong?

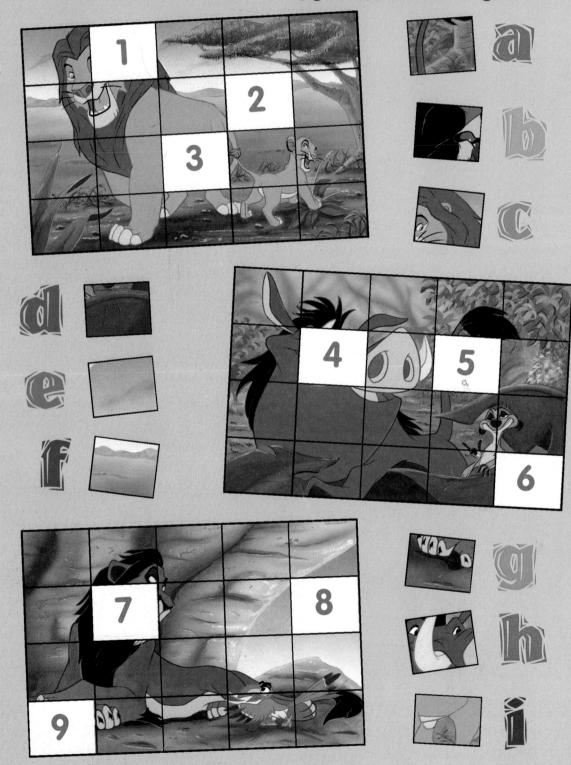

40

Zebra crossing

Help Simba reach Nala
by finding the way
through the white stripes on the zebras.

The feast finders

Timon and Pumba have found a feast of bugs!
See if you can solve all of these tasty puzzles.

1 What number should go in the blank space?

2 Which caterpillar adds up to the highest number?

3 Which of these details does not appear in the picture?

42

4 Which two butterflies are the same?

5 How many berries are in the bushes?

6 How many bugs with red spots can you count?

Answers:
1. 40. 2. a. 3. e. 4. d and g. 5. 11. 6. Two.

43

A charming tail

One afternoon, Aladdin and Abu were walking through Agrabah's market. They noticed a large crowd of people watching a snake charmer. "Come on, Abu, this looks like good fun!" said Aladdin.

The snake charmer sat cross-legged on the ground holding a small flute in his hands. In front of him was a wicker basket. The snake charmer began playing the flute. As the music filled the air, the head of a deadly-looking snake rose out of the basket. The snake stretched up and began to sway and dance along to the tune. The trembling crowd gasped in amazement. But Abu wasn't watching the snake charmer or the snake - he was looking at a group of guards who were in the crowd. One of them was eating a big, juicy apple. It looked so delicious that Abu climbed up a wall and dangled down right above the guard's head. "Oh, no," thought Aladdin, "Abu's going to get us into trouble!" When the guard went to take another bite of the apple, Abu swung in front of him and bit it first. The guard drew his sword and shouted, "Catch that monkey!" Abu jumped into Aladdin's arms and the guards rushed forward. "I think it's time we left," gulped Aladdin. He sprinted off through the market.

Aladdin realised that the guards were still following close behind. "We won't be able to out-run them, Abu," said Aladdin. "I'd better think of something fast!" Aladdin spotted a stall that had some old junk on it - this gave Aladdin an idea. He grabbed an old pot and a straw and ran around the corner. He put the pot on the ground and said, "Quick, Abu, climb inside!" Abu dived into the pot and curled up at the bottom. Just then, the angry guards came charging around the corner and saw Aladdin by the pot. "The monkey must be hiding in there!" said one of the guards. They raised their swords and got ready to move in. Aladdin sat cross-legged on the ground and said, "Don't get too close to the dangerous snake in the pot - its bite is deadlier than a hundred sharp swords!" The guards looked nervously at each other. "Don't listen to him," the leader shouted, "there's no snake in there! He's just protecting the monkey."

When the guards stepped forward, Aladdin put the straw to his mouth and began to whistle down it. The guard shrieked when a long snake-like shape rose up from the pot and began swaying to the tune. "There *is* a snake in there!" one of the guards said. All the guards backed away and decided to look elsewhere for Abu. When they were gone, Aladdin laughed and said, "It's safe to come out, Abu. Lucky for you they didn't get close enough to notice that the deadly snake was really just your wiggling tail!"

the end

Reach the lamp

Who will win the race to get to the magical lamp?
If Jafar gets there before Aladdin or Abu,
it will mean big trouble for everyone in Agrabah!
Play this game on your own or with two friends.

How to play

Place a counter on each of the three characters. Take turns flipping a coin. If it shows heads, you move up a number. If it shows tails you move down a number. The first character to reach the lamp is the winner!

5

4

3

3

2

1

1

Aladdin

Ribbon route

Aladdin has a secret meeting with Jasmine, but he could end up in big trouble if he follows some of these ribbons. Which ribbon should Aladdin follow to reach Jasmine safely?

a   b   c   d   e   f

Answer: Ribbon e.

48